AN INTRODUCTION TO

Modern Mathematics

PRENTICE-HALL MATHEMATICS SERIES

Dr. Albert A. Bennett, Editor

AN INTRODUCTION TO
Modern Mathematics

ROBERT W. SLOAN

Professor of Mathematics
State University of New York
College of Education at Oswego

1960
Englewood Cliffs, N. J.
PRENTICE-HALL, INC.

PRINTED IN THE UNITED STATES OF AMERICA
48829

To PAULINE, ELLA, MARILYN, ABIGAIL *and* PRISCILLA

Preface

All of us have heard the expression "modern mathematics," as applied to introductory mathematics, many times during our academic careers. Unfortunately, some of us have felt that modern mathematics means complicated mathematics and, because of this, have tended to disregard the advances made in the field in recent years.

This book has as its major purpose the development of elementary mathematics from a modern point of view. In keeping with this objective, I have attempted to avoid the two pitfalls which are common to most books on this subject: either they do not contain sufficient exposition of the basic principles of elementary mathematics, or they contain so much of it that they become almost useless for the reader who is not an advanced student. In addition to these considerations, I have selected my choice of subject matter in the hope that this book may be useful as a reference for high school teachers of mathematics.

My intention is not to give a detailed treatment of all the topics covered herein, and I have assumed that the reader already has some familiarity with the elementary mathematics included in an advanced high school course.

I am greatly indebted to my former colleagues at Carleton

college, especially to Professor Frank L. Wolf, for their many helpful suggestions during the writing of the manuscript. I am also indebted to the ideas in the curriculum developed by the University of Illinois Committee on School Mathematics for some of the rather unusual methods involved in the presentation of a number of the topics.

Finally, I wish to thank my wife, who served as proofreader, critic, and advisor.

R.W.S.

Contents

chapter 1

INTRODUCTION

1.1	*Modern Mathematics*	1
1.2	*Things and Names*	3
1.3	*Numbers*	5
1.4	*Arabic Numerals*	7

chapter 2

SETS AND SENTENCES

2.1	*Sets*	10
2.2	*More About Sets*	11
2.3	*Sentences and Variables*	14

ix

SETS AND SENTENCES (CONT.)

2.4 *Compound Sentences* 16

2.5 *Intuition and Formalism* 19

2.6 *Arguments* 22

2.7 *All and Some* 24

2.8 *Axioms—We Assume* 26

chapter 3

NUMBERS, EQUATIONS, AND GRAPHS

3.1 *Directed Numbers* 30

3.2 *Subtracting Directed Numbers* 34

3.3 *Ordering Directed Numbers* 35

3.4 *The Number Line* 37

3.5 *Absolute Value* 38

3.6 *Mathematical Confusion* 39

3.7 *Equations and Inequalities* 40

3.8 *Graphs* 42

chapter 4

ORDERED PAIRS, FUNCTIONS, AND RELATIONS

4.1 *Ordered Pairs* 44

4.2 *Open Sentences in Two Variables* 46

4.3 *Lines and Linear Equations* 48

4.4 *Relations* 50

4.5 *Functions* 51

4.6 *Composition of Functions* 53

ORDERED PAIRS, FUNCTIONS, AND RELATIONS (CONT.)

4.7   *Inverses of Functions*   *54*

4.8   *Principal Values*   *56*

chapter 5

SPECIAL FUNCTIONS

5.1   *The Bracket Function*   *58*

5.2   *The Exponential Function*   *59*

5.3   *Mathematical Induction*   *60*

5.4   *Extension of the Exponential Function*   *62*

5.5   *The Inverse of the Exponential Function*   *65*

BIBLIOGRAPHY   *67*

INDEX   *71*

AN INTRODUCTION TO

Modern Mathematics

1

Introduction

1.1 MODERN MATHEMATICS

In this book we are going to examine the elements of mathematics from a modern point of view. Before we commence, it might be of interest for us to inquire as to just what is meant here by the word "modern." To many people, when we talk about modern mathematics, we are talking about mathematics that is better than "old-fashioned" mathematics, since if it is "modern" it is automatically "the best." This attitude would force us to accept the fact that one of our highly chromed autos of today is automatically a better car than the Model T, a fact which is doubtful if not downright untrue. To answer the question: "Is modern mathematics an improvement, and if so, why?" is part of the function of this book, but in a certain sense the question misses the point.

Over the years, mathematicians have tried to improve their

knowledge of their subject, and with each advance there have arisen new questions concerning the foundations upon which mathematics is built. The standards of rigor have changed from Newton's day when it was perfectly all right to state things which seemed to be intuitively obvious without proof. It was not until some of these intuitively obvious facts were shown to be false that mathematicians began to question their assumptions. In order to question the assumptions, it was often necessary to state an intuitive notion quite precisely. When this was done, it soon became obvious that a better understanding of mathematics demanded a language that was as precise as man could make it.

A good part of "modern" mathematics has been concerned with this cleaning up of the language, but unfortunately, this precision has been in the past relegated to the graduate schools on the assumption that students with less training are incapable of understanding precise language. It is exactly the fact that even grade school students have shown themselves to be capable of understanding precise language that has led to the recent wide interest in "modern mathematics," or, to put it a little differently, "precise mathematics."

Let me add, lest you get the wrong impression, that what I have been talking about above is only one aspect of modern mathematics. Throughout history, one of the great driving forces in mathematics has been the search for generality. In recent years, this search, along with the attempt to solve new problems, has had a profound effect on mathematics. A great part of modern mathematics deals with subjects which were unknown 100 years ago.

With these ideas in mind, we are going to study the basic ideas of elementary algebra in order to increase our understanding of the subject matter and incidentally to increase if possible the precision and generality of the subject.

1.2 THINGS AND NAMES

In order to communicate, man has devised a system of sounds which name concepts and things and a means of putting these names together to form ideas. This system varies from place to place and is called the language. In order to facilitate communication and also to help him remember, man has also devised a means of writing the names of these things on paper or blackboard. One difficulty that has arisen from the use of writing has been the question of differentiating between things and the marks on the paper which name these things. Ordinarily there is no difficulty in determining what is meant by a given sentence but sometimes confusion can arise when a clear distinction is not made between things and their names.

There are many examples of what can happen if confusion between names and things is allowed, some of them in the form of riddles to which most of you have at one time been exposed. For example:

What is 1 and 1? Answer, 11 (not 2)
What is the longest word in English? Answer, S*mile*s
What is half of eight? Answer, 3 (the right half)

When you read the words George Washington, you think of the man. If the person who wrote the words intends that you should think of the words themselves, he must let you know in some way. There are many possible ways, for example, capitalizing or drawing a circle around the word. Throughout this book, when we want to indicate the symbol or name instead of the thing which the symbol names, we will indicate this by putting single quotes around the symbol. With this convention, the above riddles become:

'1' and '1' is '11'.
Smiles is the longest word in English because there is a 'mile' between the first and last letter.

'3' is the right half of '8'.

Consider the following and note the uses of the single quotation marks:

> Everyone drinks water. It is unlikely that anyone could drink 'water'. Water will put out fire but 'water' will not put out fire. If you wanted to put 'water' on a fire, you would have to write 'water' on a piece of paper and drop it into the fire. The city water works has water in it. The city water works has a sign outside with 'water' on it.

It is evident that, in order to avoid confusion, we should use semi-quotes whenever we are referring to the name of a thing instead of the thing itself. However, on the theory that it's all right to say "ain't" if you know better, we will sometimes omit the semi-quotes if no confusion can arise.

We will use the symbol '=' throughout to mean that the symbols which appear on either side of the symbol '=' are both names for the same number. Thus we can write $(5 - 3) + 6 = 2 + 6$ because '2' is another name for the number named by '$5 - 3$'.

PROBLEMS

1.2.1 Punctuate the following so that they make sense:

a) Joe has a book.
b) Bill found a book in a book.
c) Fourteen is an even number.
d) You can write 9 instead of writing $12 - 3$.
e) 2 is part of 23.
f) I put $\frac{6}{2}$ in the blank space.
g) You can add $\frac{1}{2}$ and $\frac{1}{3}$ but you can't add $\frac{1}{2}$ and $\frac{1}{3}$.
h) To multiply by 10, add a 0.
i) Move the decimal point in 7.352 3 places to the right.
j) The blackboard does not have single quotes around it.

1.2.2 Discuss carefully the following argument:

a) 2 divides the denominator of $\frac{4}{6}$.

b) $\frac{4}{6} = \frac{2}{3}$.

Thus

c) 2 divides the denominator of $\frac{2}{3}$.

Thus

d) 2 divides 3.

1.3 NUMBERS

In view of the remarks in the preceding section, the question naturally arises: If the number 2 is not a mark on the paper, just what is the number 2?

Let us suppose that a teacher in a class wants to know whether there are more chairs in a classroom than students. He can solve the problem easily by having the students sit down and if there are chairs left over then there are more chairs than students and vice versa. This matching process, simple as it is, is a very important one in mathematics. Two finite sets are the same size if they can be matched or paired with no members left over. One finite set is of smaller size than another if and only if it can be matched with a set consisting of part of the members of the second. If two sets can be matched or paired off, the mathematician says that these sets are in 1 to 1 correspondence or that the two sets are equivalent.

A shrewd farmer may be able to tell at a glance when one cow is more valuable than another but if he wants to obtain the more valuable cow, he needs to know values in terms of money. In other words, he needs a standard scale. Let us try to construct a standard scale for our sizes of sets.

Consider the following collections of symbols:

$$\{+\}$$
$$\{+, \$\}$$
$$\{+, \$, \delta\}$$
$$\{+, \$, \delta, \theta\} \quad \text{and so forth.}$$

If a set can be matched with the collection of symbols in the first set, we say the given set has one element. If a set is matchable with the set {+, $}, we say that the number of elements in the given set is two, and so forth.

The symbols which we used in our standard sets are to a certain extent unfamiliar and thus hard to remember and use. So we will ordinarily use the following standard sets of symbols:

$$\{`1'\}$$
$$\{`1', `2'\}$$
$$\{`1', `2', `3'\}$$
$$\{`1', `2', `3', `4'\} \quad \text{and so forth.}$$

In order to make life a little easier for ourselves, we make a correspondence between our standard sets of symbols and the symbols themselves in the following way:

$$\{`1'\} \qquad\qquad \leftrightarrow `1'$$
$$\{`1', `2'\} \qquad\quad \leftrightarrow `2'$$
$$\{`1', `2', `3'\} \qquad \leftrightarrow `3'$$
$$\{`1', `2', `3', `4'\} \leftrightarrow `4' \quad \text{and so forth.}$$

Thus when we write the symbol '4', we are referring to a whole class of sets, each of which can be matched with a set consisting of the symbols '1', '2', '3', '4'. We are counting!

Note that all we need to be able to count is a set of symbols going on forever (the set of symbols cannot stop lest we be unable to count sets larger than the set of symbols). In our conventional decimal system, we use only ten different symbols and by using certain combinations of these symbols, we can write names for all the counting numbers. (Or, to put it differently, we can construct a standard set of any size whatever.) Arithmetic (calculation with these symbols) is really a study of the decimal system rather than the study of numbers.

1.4 ARABIC NUMERALS

The question of the origin and use of the symbols which we used in the preceding section to construct our standard sets is a complex one including the early history of man, and is a question which we cannot discuss without some danger of oversimplifying the historical currents which determined the growth of arithmetic as we know it today. It is possible, however, for us to conjecture, on the basis of known facts, how the present symbolism for numbers developed.

Primitive man must have used his fingers to count, and as long as the arithmetic he had to do was fairly simple it is probable that he found this quite satisfactory. Some ancient tycoon must have found, however, that he owned more sheep than it was possible to count using his fingers, and thus he was forced to use pebbles (note that the set of fingers or the set of pebbles served as standard sets for our cave man). In neolithic times, man began to trade, and this required that he be able to handle larger and larger numbers. It was sometime during this period that one of the greatest civilizing inventions of all, the abacus, was made. The idea behind the abacus was fairly simple. If a man was counting using pebbles, he counted up to nine and then instead of laying down a tenth pebble in the same pile, he picked up the pile of nine pebbles and laid down one pebble in a second pile. Thus, by using a fewer number of pebbles, he was able to count much higher than he could before. For example, five pebbles in the second pile and four pebbles in the first pile was equivalent to fifty four pebbles in a single pile.

The Romans developed an abacus which used intermediate piles, with one pebble in the intermediate pile standing for five pebbles in the first pile, and one pebble in the second pile standing for two pebbles in the intermediate pile. (This process still left one pebble in the second pile standing for ten pebbles in the first pile.) The actual abacus consisted of a table with lines or grooves for placing pebbles as shown in Figure 1.4.1 (the intermediate piles were placed above the basic piles). The number represented in the figure is three units, one five, two tens, one fifty, four hundreds and one five hundred, or nine hundred seventy eight. Since the processes of arithmetic can be derived from counting, it is fairly obvious that we can calculate using the abacus. In fact, our word calculate derives from the Latin word *calculus*, meaning pebble.

The rise of commerce forced another invention upon early man, the keeping of records. In order to remember the results

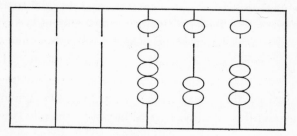

Fig. 1.4.1

of a calculation on the abacus, the merchant of the late Stone Age found it necessary to invent symbols to represent the configuration of the stones on his counter. Early attempts at this representation resulted in what was essentially a picture of the abacus with the answer displayed on clay or papyrus. More sophistication led to such things as Roman numerals. (The number represented in Figure 1.4.1 was written DCCCCLXXVIII.) Needless to say, this system of writing symbols for numbers was awkward, for, even with Roman numerals, new symbols had to be invented for each column added to the abacus.

It was not until much later, when the Hindus invented a system involving ten symbols, one of the ten indicating an empty column on the abacus, that our present system of numeration originated. (The system was introduced to Western Europe by the Muslims, thus the name, Arabic numerals.)* Even later, it was discovered that the notation was particularly adaptable for calculation without the use of the abacus, and thus the science of arithmetic was born.

As we mentioned at the start of this section, the picture which we have just drawn may have many inaccuracies but there seems to be no doubt that the general development of our system of naming numbers was substantially as we have outlined it.

PROBLEMS

1.4.1 Using a piece of paper and checkers or pebbles or bits of colored paper, construct an abacus. Describe its use, develop a symbolism for writing the results of a calculation, and perform some calculations on the abacus.

1.4.2 Discuss the kind of arithmetic which we would have today if our ancestors had had four fingers on each hand instead of five. What kind of an abacus would have been used?

* It is probably true that the Indian abacus did not have the intermediate piles characteristic of the Roman abacus. Thus the system of ten numerals rather than a combination of fives and tens as in Roman numerals.

2

·
·
·
·
·

Sets and Sentences

·
·
·
·
·
·
·
·

2.1 SETS

In order to talk about numbers, we had to introduce the concept of a set, which is a basic concept in mathematics. In fact, the idea of a set is even more basic than the idea of a number in spite of the fact that numbers are usually thought to be the main concern of mathematics.

Ordinarily we will think of a set as a collection of objects; the individual members of the set are called its elements. We shall hereafter write '$a \in A$' when we mean that a is an element of the set A. We write '$a \notin A$' to mean that a is not an element of A.

Suppose we wish to name the set whose elements are the numbers 1, 2, and 3. We could always say: The set whose elements are the numbers 1, 2, 3; but in order to shorten the description, we write $\{1,2,3\}$. Thus: $1 \in \{1,2\}$, $\theta \in \{\theta\}$, $3 \notin \{2,4\}$. Note that a set is completely determined once we know all its elements.

In fact, if two sets have the same elements, we say that they are equal.

The concepts of 'set' and 'property' are to a certain extent interchangeable since it is always the case that properties determine sets and sets determine properties.* Consider the property expressed by the sentence: "He is a farmer" and the set having for its elements all farmers. Any individual which has the property belongs to the set and vice versa. In fact, nearly every property determines a set, namely the set of things which have the property, and every set determines a property, namely the property of belonging to the set.

PROBLEMS

2.1.1 Write several sentences describing properties and describe the sets corresponding to these properties.

2.1.2 Using the notation which we introduced above, name the set:

    a) consisting of the positive integers between 2 and 9.
    b) consisting of the solutions of $x^2 = 25$.
    c) consisting of the solution of $x = 3$.

2.1.3 Describe in words:

    a) $\{1\}$.
    b) $\{a,b,c,d\}$.
    c) $\{3,5,7,11,13\}$.

2.1.4 The set $\{1,2,3,4\}$ has some resemblance to one of the standard sets of Section 1.3. Are these the same? Discuss.

2.2 MORE ABOUT SETS

In talking about sets, we must remember that the set and its elements are two different things. For example, during the Civil

---

* We should note that a given set may determine or be determined by several superficially different properties.

War, Lincoln, with one stroke of his pen, abolished the set of all slaves, but the individual members of the set (its elements) continued in good health. The distinction is particularly important when talking about sets of one element.

It may happen, in talking about two sets A and B, that every element of A is also an element of B. When this happens we say that A is contained in B or *A is a subset of B*. In symbols this is written '$A \subseteq B$'. (Note that it is trivially true that any set is a subset of itself. Symbolically, $A \subseteq A$.) Given two sets, A and B, A is said to be a *proper subset* of B if A is a subset of B and furthermore there is an element of B which is not in A. If A is a proper subset of B, we write '$A \subset B$'.

Consider again two sets A and B. We define a new set called *the intersection of A and B* (we write '$A \cap B$') which is the set of those objects which belong simultaneously to A and B. For example, if A is the set of all real numbers between 0 and 1 and B is the set of all rational numbers, $A \cap B$ is the set of all numbers which are rational and between 0 and 1 (i.e., the set of all proper fractions). Since it is true that an element of $A \cap B$ must be in A, it follows that $A \cap B \subseteq A$.

If A and B are sets, we define a new set called *the union of A and B* (we write '$A \cup B$') which is the set of those objects which belong to at least one of the sets A and B. For example, if A is the set of chairs in one room of a two room apartment, and B is the set of chairs in the other room, $A \cup B$ is the set of chairs in the apartment. Since it is true that any element of A is in A $\cup$ B, it follows that $A \subseteq A \cup B$.

If A is a set, we define a new set called *the complement of A* (we write 'A''') which is the set of all things not in A.

The words, all things not in A, in the above paragraph can lead to confusion unless we are careful. Do we really mean *all* things, or do we mean that we should restrict ourselves somewhat? Evidently we don't want to include all things so we define *the universal set* (written '*U*') as the set which has the totality of elements *under discussion* as its members. Also, for convenience, we introduce the *empty set* (also called the null set and written '*φ*') which has no elements. Note that the complement of the universal set is the empty set, that the empty set is a subset of every set and that every set is a subset of the universal set.

PROBLEMS

Let $A = \{1,3,4,5\}$, $B = \{1,2,3\}$, $C = \{2,5,6\}$, $D = \{2\}$, and $U = \{1,2,3,4,5,6,7\}$. Find:

2.2.1 $A \cup B$.

2.2.2 $A \cap B$.

2.2.3 $(A \cup B) \cap C$.

2.2.4 $(A \cap C) \cup (B \cap C)$.

2.2.5 $A \cup D$.

2.2.6 $A \cap D$.

2.2.7 $(B \cup D) \cup (A \cup C)$.

2.2.8 A'.

2.2.9 $(A' \cup B')'$ (compare your answer with 2.2.2).

2.2.10 $(A \cup D)'$.

2.2.11 $A' \cap D'$ (compare your answer with 2.2.10).

2.2.12 $(A')'$.

2.2.13 Look at 2.2.10 and 2.2.11 and make a conjecture. Can you prove this?

2.2.14 Two sets are identical (written $A = B$) if they have the same elements. Show that $A = B$ if and only if $A \subseteq B$ and $B \subseteq A$.

2.2.15 Show that A is a proper subset of B if and only if $A \subseteq B$ and $B \nsubseteq A$.

2.3 SENTENCES AND VARIABLES

In a previous section, we mentioned that properties and sets were interchangeable concepts. That this is so is not hard to see, but it is also true that properties are in general described by sentences of a certain type. If this is the case, then in a certain sense, sentences and sets will be interchangeable concepts.

Consider the expression: ———— is a teacher. Notice that the expression has the form of a sentence except that the subject of the verb is a blank instead of a name. If, however, I write the name of a person in the blank, the sentence becomes meaningful and indeed, can be answered true or false. A little thought should convince you that most properties are described by expressions of the above type. Such expressions are often referred to as *open sentences.*

Notice that the open sentence above can take on either a true value or a false value depending on the name written in the blank. If, for example, I write "R. Sloan" in the blank, the sentence is true; but if I write "Ulysses S. Grant", the sentence is false. If, when I write the name of a person in the blank, the sentence becomes a true one, that person is said to *satisfy the sentence.* Notice that any open sentence picks out a set of objects, namely those objects which satisfy the sentence. Thus we see that every open sentence (with certain minor exceptions) determines a set called *the solution set of the sentence.* From our preceding remarks, we could just as well have said that every open sentence defines a property, namely, the property of belonging to the solution set of the open sentence.

The blank in the open sentence is a very special object whose purpose is to hold a place for names of things. These blanks are important enough that they are given a special name; they are called *variables!* The set of things whose names are written in place of the blank is called the *domain of the variable.* It is customary, especially in mathematics, to use the letters of the alphabet instead of blanks for variables, but the meaning is still the same. *A variable is a place holder for names of things.*

As we mentioned above, every open sentence determines a set, the set of things which satisfy the open sentence. If we are given the open sentence *x is a teacher*, we can name the solution set of the sentence by saying: "the set consisting of all people who satisfy the sentence *x is a teacher*," but it will be to our advantage to introduce a shorthand notation for this set. Instead of the rather long sentence above we write '$\{x|x$ *is a teacher*$\}$'.*

Consider the open sentence $3 + x = 1$. If we consider that the domain of the variable is the set of all real numbers, then the solution set is the set $\{-2\}$. But if we consider that the domain of the variable is the set of all positive real numbers, then the solution set is the empty set, ϕ. It is therefore quite important that the domain of the variables be specified when naming members of the solution set of an open sentence. (In this text, in all cases with open sentences involving numbers, if the domain is not specified, it is understood to be the set of all real numbers for which the defining sentence is meaningful.)

PROBLEMS

List the elements of the following sets:

2.3.1 $\{x|x$ even and x positive and x is less than $10\}$.

2.3.2 $\{x|2x = -36\}$.

2.3.3 $\{y|2y = -36\}$.

2.3.4 $\{t|2 + t = 0$ and t positive$\}$.

2.3.5 $\{-|-^2 = 25\}$.

2.3.6 $\{x|x + 3 = 3\}$.

2.3.7 $\{x|x$ positive$\} \cap \{x|2 + x = 0\}$ (see 2.3.4).

* This symbol is read: the set of all x's such that x is a teacher.

2.3.8 $\{r|r^2 = 25$ or $r^2 = 16\}$.

2.3.9 $\{r|r^2 = 25\} \cup \{s|s^2 = 16\}$ (see 2.3.8).

Find a sentence whose solution set is the given set:

2.3.10 $\{1\}$.

2.3.11 $\{7,9,11\}$.

2.3.12 $\{19,23,29,31,37,41\}$.

2.4 COMPOUND SENTENCES

When we defined the symbols '$\cap$' and '$\cup$', we were required to use the words *and* and *or*. In this section we will examine more closely the properties of these words (called logical connectives) which make compound sentences.

When we discuss a connective, it will be necessary for us to know just how the truth of a compound sentence depends on the truth of its components. For example: If we want to describe the properties of 'and', we consider the sentence P *and* Q. (In this section and what follows, we will let P, Q, R, and so forth stand for sentences. That is, P, Q, R, and so forth, are variables whose domains are the set of declarative sentences.) Now P can be either true or false, and so can Q. If a sentence P is true then we say that its truth value is T; if it is false we say that its truth value is F. Thus, there are 4 possible pairs of truth values for these two statements and we want to know in each case whether the statement P *and* Q is true or false. The answer can best be displayed by a table (called a truth table) listing all the possibilities for P and Q and the resultant truth values for P *and* Q. (Since to write the word *and* requires time and effort, we shall henceforth use the symbol '$\wedge$' between sentences in place of 'and'. Thus the sentence P *and* Q will be written '$P \wedge Q$'.)

Below we see the truth table for $P \wedge Q$ (also called the **conjunction** of P and Q):

P	Q	$P \wedge Q$
T	T	T
T	F	F
F	T	F
F	F	F

Table 2.4.1

Note that $P \wedge Q$ is true only when both P and Q are true; otherwise it is false.

Consider next the sentence *not* P (or the **negation** of P, written '$\sim P$'):

P	$\sim P$
T	F
F	T

Table 2.4.2

Note that $\sim P$ is false when P is true and vice versâ.

Next, let us consider the sentence P *or* Q, called the **disjunction** of P and Q. Here the situation is complicated slightly by the fact that there are in general two different meanings for *It is raining or it is snowing*. The dictionary says that the sentence above is false if it is both raining and snowing. For reasons which will become apparent later (see Problem 2.5.2) we will purposely define P *or* Q in a slightly different way. (As in the case of P *and* Q, we introduce a symbol, '$\vee$', to stand for 'or'. Thus P *or* Q is written '$P \vee Q$'.)

P	Q	$P \lor Q$
T	T	T
T	F	T
F	T	T
F	F	F

Table 2.4.3

Note that $P \lor Q$ can be translated as *P and/or Q.*

With these basic tables, we can construct truth tables for more complicated sentences. For example, the table for $\sim(P \land \sim Q)$ can be constructed as follows:

P	Q	$\sim Q$	$P \land \sim Q$	$\sim(P \land \sim Q)$
T	T	F	F	T
T	F	T	T	F
F	T	F	F	T
F	F	T	F	T

Table 2.4.4

It must be apparent by now that it is no accident that the symbol ' $\land$ ' and the symbol ' $\cap$ ' are very closely related. In fact the symbol ' $\land$ ' could have been used to define ' $\cap$ ' in the following way: $x \in A \cap B$ means $x \in A \land x \in B$.

If we let Px and Qx stand for open sentences (x is the variable in the sentence) then we can define ' $\cap$ ' in still another way:

$$\{x|Px\} \cap \{x|Qx\} = \{x|Px \land Qx\}$$

Similarly: $$\{x|Px\} \cup \{x|Qx\} = \{x|Px \lor Qx\}$$

and: $$\{x|Px\}' = \{x|\sim Px\}$$

PROBLEMS

Construct a truth table for each of the following:

2.4.1 $\sim(P \lor Q) \lor \sim(Q \lor P)$.

2.4.2 $\sim(P \vee Q) \wedge P$.

2.4.3 $\sim(P \vee Q)$.

2.4.4 $\sim P \wedge \sim Q$ (see 2.4.3 and 2.2.11).

2.4.5 $\sim(P \wedge Q)$.

2.4.6 $\sim P \vee \sim Q$ (see 2.4.5 and 2.2.9).

2.4.7 $(P \wedge (Q \vee R)) \vee (R \wedge Q)$ (Hint: how many possibilities are there?)

2.5 INTUITION AND FORMALISM

Suppose we wish to make a statement which is not an outright assertion, but rather an assertion containing a condition. For example: "If it is nice then I will take a walk", or "If I had the money, I would buy a car". Both of these statements are of the form *If P then Q* and are called **conditional statements.** (We write '$P \Rightarrow Q$'.)* Again, the symbol '$\Rightarrow$' is completely defined if we specify the truth values of $P \Rightarrow Q$ for all values of P and Q:

P	Q	$P \Rightarrow Q$
T	T	T
T	F	F
F	T	T
F	F	T

Table 2.5.1

It is important here to note that no causal connection is intended in the use of '$\Rightarrow$'. The meaning is contained in the table and nothing more is intended. It might, however, be helpful to discuss some of the basic problems inherent in our rather strange definition of '$\Rightarrow$'.

In any attempt to set up definitions of the logical connectives, our biggest difficulties are at the beginning. We are dealing with

* The symbol '$P \Rightarrow Q$' may be read: if P then Q, or P implies Q.

the human mind in all its obtuseness and any attempt by us to
make precise the ideas and intuitions of individuals will be handi-
capped because each individual has his own ideas concerning
the use of the words we are attempting to define. It would seem
we face an impossible task. We can, however, overcome some of
this difficulty by being, to a certain extent, arbitrary. We pick
definitions of our concepts by using, insofar as is possible, the
average of the standards of many individuals. (One way to do
this would be to define the connectives by a majority vote.)
For example, the idea expressed by the word *implies* is a concept
that can have many meanings and we must choose a definition
that corresponds to the intuitive idea of 'implies' of as many
people as possible. Even if we attempt this solution, we still
have difficult problems, because a given individual may have an
idea of the meaning of 'implies' which allows him to say, for example, whether a given step in the proof of a theorem is correct,
and yet be unable to tell whether his idea of implication and our
definition of implication are equivalent.

The only way to convince the doubter of the equivalence of
his intuitive notion of implication and our precise definition of it
is to show him that in a large number of cases the two agree.
We will not give many examples to convince the doubter here;
we will just comment that many examples can be given to show
that our precise definition of the logical connectives does in most
cases agree with what most people feel is the correct use of these
connectives. In the case of '∧', '∨' and '∼', there is no great
difficulty, since there is almost unanimous agreement on the
meanings of these connectives, and most people are convinced
that their intuitive notion corresponds with our precise definition. The definition of '⇒', however, creates a problem which
we must try to settle.

Consider the compound open sentence: "If *x* is a man, then
x is a human being." We would want to say that this is a true

sentence for all substitutions for x. Yet if we substitute for x the name of an elephant, both the hypothesis and the conclusion are false (and we still want the whole sentence to be true). Also if we substitute the name of a woman for x, the hypothesis is false and the conclusion is true (and we still want the whole sentence to be true). These considerations lead us to conclude that the definition we have given for '$\Rightarrow$' is the only one possible, given the requirements which we want '$\Rightarrow$' to fulfill.

We define one more logical connective, *P if and only if Q* (written '$P \Leftrightarrow Q$'):

P	Q	$P \Leftrightarrow Q$
T	T	T
T	F	F
F	T	F
F	F	T

Table 2.5.2

Note the '$P \Leftrightarrow Q$' says essentially that P and Q have the same truth values.

In constructing complicated compound sentences using the logical connectives, it is important to make use of signs for grouping, such as parentheses and brackets, because their elimination may lead to considerable confusion. For example: $P \Rightarrow Q \wedge R$ can mean either $(P \Rightarrow Q) \wedge R$ or $P \Rightarrow (Q \wedge R)$, and these two sentences do not have the same truth values.

PROBLEMS

2.5.1 Construct a truth table for each of the following:

a) $P \Rightarrow (Q \vee R)$.

b) $(P \Rightarrow Q) \vee R$.

c) $(P \Rightarrow Q) \Leftrightarrow (P \wedge Q)$.

d) $(P \Leftrightarrow Q) \Leftrightarrow [(P \Rightarrow Q) \wedge (Q \Rightarrow P)]$.

e) $\sim(P \wedge Q) \Leftrightarrow (\sim P \vee \sim Q)$.

f) $\sim(P \vee Q) \Leftrightarrow (\sim P \wedge \sim Q)$.

g) $\sim(P \Rightarrow Q) \Leftrightarrow (P \wedge \sim Q)$.

h) $[P \wedge (Q \vee R)] \Leftrightarrow [(P \wedge Q) \vee (P \wedge R)]$.

2.5.2 We define $P \underline{\vee} Q$ by the following truth table:

P	Q	$P \underline{\vee} Q$
T	T	F
T	F	T
F	T	T
F	F	F

Table 2.5.3

Construct a truth table for

$$\sim(P \underline{\vee} Q) \Leftrightarrow [(\sim P \wedge \sim Q) \vee (P \wedge Q)].$$

2.6 ARGUMENTS

Look at Problems 2.5.1 (*d*) through 2.5.1 (*h*) and 2.5.2. If you have done them right, the truth values of the compound sentences listed are all T. This means that regardless of the truth values of *P*, *Q*, and *R*, the compound sentences above always have truth value T. To say the same thing in a different way, the truth of the compound sentences depends only on the form of the sentences and not on the meaning assigned to *P*, *Q*, and *R*. Such sentences are called *tautologies.*

One of the most important uses of logic is that of checking arguments. We mean by an *argument* the assertion that a certain statement (called the conclusion) follows from others (called premises). An argument is said to be *valid* if and only if the conjunction of the premises implies the conclusion.

At this point we are going to make use of our intuition and its relation to the formal definition which we have made in the preceding sections. You have probably thought of the laws of logic as the rules of sentence structure which tell us how to get new sentences from old. That is, if we follow the laws of logic, we cannot derive "wrong" statements from a collection of "right" statements. It is a theorem in logic that, if we assume the usual basic rules of reasoning, these rules and all the rules derivable from them are tautologies; furthermore, if a statement is a tautology, it is derivable from the basic rules. Thus we may say that an argument is valid if and only if *the conjunction of the premises implies the conclusion* is a tautology!

We will write arguments by first listing the premises, then drawing a line and then writing the conclusion. For example:

> If it is raining, I will not go.
> It is raining.
> _____
> I will not go.

is an argument written in the form which we have specified.

The argument above is an example of a type of argument of the form:

$$P \Rightarrow Q$$
$$\frac{P}{Q}$$

and is a valid argument because $[(P \Rightarrow Q) \wedge P] \Rightarrow Q$ is a tautology.

We should note here that symbolic logic is useful only in checking the validity of arguments. It is of no use in the construction of valid arguments. Another way of saying this is that although we can check a statement to see if it is a tautology, logic provides no guide for us to construct new tautologies.

PROBLEMS

Check the validity of the following arguments:

2.6.1 $P \vee Q$
$$\frac{\sim P}{Q}$$

2.6.2 $P \Rightarrow Q$
$$\frac{\sim R \Rightarrow \sim Q}{\sim R \Rightarrow \sim P}$$

2.6.3 $P \Rightarrow Q$
$$\frac{\sim Q}{\sim P}$$

2.6.4 $P \Rightarrow Q$
$$\frac{\sim P \Rightarrow \sim Q}{P \Leftrightarrow Q}$$

2.6.5 $P \Rightarrow Q$
$\sim P \Rightarrow \sim Q$
$$\frac{P \wedge \sim Q}{R}$$

2.6.6   If this is a good book, it is worth reading.
The problems are easy or the book is not worth reading.
The problems are easy.
This is a good book.

2.6.7   It is not true that it is raining and snowing.
It is not snowing.
It is raining.

2.7 ALL AND SOME

During our discussion of the conditional, we used a concept which is quite important and used in mathematics in almost every statement. In order to understand much of what is done in mathematics, this concept must be thoroughly understood.

We already know that open sentences do not have truth values. In fact, in order to assign a truth value to an open sentence we must first fill in the blank. However, we would like to be able to say that the open sentence $x^2 - 4 = (x - 2)(x + 2)$ is in some sense a true sentence. What we mean here is that if we substitute the name for any number for x, we will get a true statement. To put it in other words: what we really mean when we say that $x^2 - 4 = (x - 2)(x + 2)$ is true is that $x^2 - 4 = (x - 2)(x + 2)$ is *true for every significant substitution for x*. (A name of a thing is a significant substitution for a variable if the thing belongs to the domain of the variable.) In a sense, you are telling the listener "how many" of the values of the open sentence are true. Such sentences are said to be quantified sentences and the words or symbols which tell us "how many" are called *quantifiers.*

We will need symbols to stand for our quantifiers since evidently they will be used a great deal in our future work in mathematics. Thus, if Px is an open sentence, we write $\forall xPx$ (read: for all x, Px) to mean *Px is true for all significant substitutions for x.*

Now it may be true that Px is true not for all x but for some x. This is written $\exists xPx$ (read: for some x, Px) and means *Px is true for some significant substitutions for x* (there may be one or more).

At this point let us investigate some of the properties of the quantifiers. These properties are essentially nothing more than restatements of the things we discussed above but let us state them specifically:

1. (Generalization) If Px is a true statement for any significant substitution for x, then $\forall xPx$ is true.

2. (Specialization) If $\forall xPx$ is a true statement and b is an element of the domain of x, then Pb is true.

3. $\forall xPx \Rightarrow \exists xPx$, if the domain of the variable is not empty.

Let us now consider what we mean when we say $\sim[\forall xPx]$. This can be translated: It is false that Px is true for every x. This is the same thing as saying: There is at least one value of x for which Px is false. Symbolically:

$$\sim[\forall xPx] \Leftrightarrow \exists x[\sim Px]$$

Similarly $$\sim[\exists xPx] \Leftrightarrow \forall x[\sim Px]$$

PROBLEMS

Restate symbolically: —

2.7.1 The square of any non-zero number is positive.

2.7.2 Every real number has an additive inverse.

2.7.3 Negate the above statements.

2.8 AXIOMS—WE ASSUME

Bertrand Russell once said: "Mathematics is the subject in which we do not know what we are talking about nor if what we say is true". This statement, although somewhat facetious, is fairly close to an accurate description of the way a mathematician looks at mathematics. What Russell was trying to do in his short statement was to give a concise statement of the axiomatic approach to mathematics. Since it is not possible to define everything*, we accept certain concepts as undefined. Since these concepts are not defined, we must in some way list the properties which we want the undefined concepts to have. The elements of this list of properties are called *axioms*. Note that, as far as the

---

* You are all aware of the circularity of dictionary definitions, for example:
   Tree—*a woody* perennial plant.
   Woody—of or pertaining to *wood*.
   Wood—the fibrous substance which makes up the greater part of the stems and branches of a *tree*.

mathematician is concerned, it is *not* necessary for the axioms to be "true" in any ordinarily accepted sense. They are assumptions about our primitive concepts and nothing more.

Given the undefined terms and the axioms concerning them, we can derive further statements about the undefined terms by using the laws of logic. These further statements are called *theorems.* You may think of an axiomatic system as a sort of giant chess game where the undefined terms are the chessmen, the axioms are the original configuration of the chessmen and the laws of logic are the rules for moving the chessmen. Any configuration which is obtainable from the original by accepted rules is called a theorem.

The basic idea of an axiom system can best be stated: *If* the axioms are accepted *and* the methods of reasoning are sound (or valid) *then* the theorems must be accepted.

If mathematics were only as we have described it above, it would be only a long and complicated game and a difficult one at that. To answer this point, let us consider that a physicist wishes to use one of the theorems in an axiomatic system. In order to use the theorem, the physicist must first interpret the undefined terms to fit his situation (e.g., he might want to interpret "point" as "electron") and then check to see if, under his interpretation, all the axioms are satisfied. If he finds this to be the case, then he can use any theorem proved in the axiomatic system as a true statement about his situation. The physicist has a *model* of the axiom system. It is apparent that the physicist will have some of the same difficulties that the logician did (Section 2.4) in showing that his physical situation is actually a model of the axiom system. The problems are slightly different in that the physicist can make fairly precise measurements of the quantities involved but in the end he is forced to admit that he can only verify by experiment, not prove, that his physical situation is a model of the axiom system.

It might be said that most mathematicians, when they are dealing with axiomatic systems, have in mind a model which they use not only to help them to visualize the axioms but also to suggest to them theorems which might be true. Thus, almost everyone who proves theorems in geometry, does so with the help of idealized pictures (i.e., a model) first of all to visualize what the axioms and theorems say and secondly to help in constructing proofs (proofs are essentially valid arguments with the axioms as the original premises). It should be noted that the pictures are not absolutely essential. Theoretically, at least, the theorems follow from the axioms using the laws of logic. The pictures are a device which we all use to assist us in constructing a proof and in understanding the theorems.

We should note here, lest the reader get the impression that all axiom systems are formalizations of rather imprecise notions, that in some cases, some axiom systems have models which are intuitively quite clear and are themselves models of "simpler" axiom systems. For example, if we can prove that the axioms of a given system are theorems of another system (or, what is the same thing, if we can derive the axioms of the first system from the axioms of the second), then a model of the second system will be a model of the first system. Such a situation exists when we prove that the axioms of Euclidean geometry can be derived from the axioms of the number system (as a matter of fact, this is exactly what we do when we consider the branch of mathematics known as analytic geometry). We say then that the set of all ordered pairs of real numbers, with the axioms of the number system, is a model of the axioms of Euclidean geometry.

Quite often, ideas are generalized by taking an axiom system and dropping one or more of the axioms. It is evident that the set of objects satisfying the old system will be a model of the new system, but it may also be true that there will exist new and different models of the new system.

PROBLEMS

2.8.1 Consider the following axiom system (due to F. L. Wolf):
Undefined terms: pot, squiggle.
Axioms:

1. Every pot is a squiggle.
2. $\forall x \, \forall y$, if x and y are squiggles, then x is a pot or y is a pot or both.
3. There is at least one pot.

Prove:

There is at least one squiggle.
There is at most one squiggle which is not a pot.

Can you find a model for this axiom system?

3

Numbers, Equations,

and Graphs

3.1 DIRECTED NUMBERS

Let us consider the following axiom system:

Undefined terms: Directed numbers.

Undefined operations: $+$ and $\cdot$

Axioms:

1 and 1′ (Closure). $\forall x \forall y$, if x and y are directed numbers, then so are $x + y$ and $x \cdot y$.

2 and 2′ (Commutative law). $\forall x \forall y$, if x and y are directed numbers, then $x + y = y + x$ and $x \cdot y = y \cdot x$.

3 and 3′ (Associative law). $\forall x \forall y \forall z$, if x, y, and z are directed numbers, then $x + (y + z) = (x + y) + z$, and $x \cdot (y \cdot z) = (x \cdot y) \cdot z$.

4 and 4′ (Identity elements). There exist numbers (designated '0' and '1') distinct from each other, such that $\forall x$, if x is a directed number, then $0 + x = x$, and $1 \cdot x = x$.

5 and 5′ (Inverse law). $\forall x$, if x is a directed number, there exist $\bar{x}$, and if $x \neq 0$, there exists x' such that $x + \bar{x} = 0$ and $x \cdot x' = 1$.

6 (Distributive law). $\forall x \forall y \forall z$, if x, y, and z are directed numbers, then $x \cdot (y + z) = x \cdot y + x \cdot z$.

Theoretically, these axioms will allow us to derive most of the properties of directed numbers which we will want to use. At least, they will allow us to perform all the operations of arithmetic. However, as we mentioned in Section 2.8, deriving theorems abstractly from a list of axioms is sometimes quite difficult; so, we will start, not from the axioms, but from what we hope is a model of the axioms.

In any attempt to construct an intuitive model for the directed numbers, we must face again the same problem which plagued us in our attempt to formalize intuitive logic. We should note before we start that any attempt to construct a model of the axioms (or, to put it another way, any attempt to derive the axioms from an intuitively constructed arithmetic) is doomed to failure. The best we can do is to make a satisfactory intuitive construction of the directed numbers which will agree with the axiomatic construction of these numbers in as many cases as possible.

With these thoughts in mind, let us imagine a road with markers one mile apart. These markers are labeled with letter symbols:

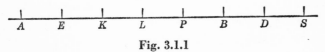

Fig. 3.1.1

If you go from A to P, you make a trip of 4 miles to the right, and if you go from S to K you make a trip of 5 miles to the left. Thus we see we have added to our concept of number by including with the length of the trip the direction in which the trip is taken. We will use the symbol '$+2$' as a name for the directed number which corresponds to all of the trips of 2 miles to the right and we will use '-2' as a name for the directed number which corresponds to all of the trips 2 miles to the left. (Note that, since we have already pre-empted the name 'directed number' for use with the axioms, we cannot officially use this word until we have defined addition and multiplication and convinced ourselves that the physical situation described is a model of the axioms. We will continue, however, to use the words 'directed number' to describe both situations, hoping, meanwhile, that no confusion will arise.) Pairs of directed numbers like $+2$ and -2, $+1.5$ and -1.5, $+13$ and -13 are called *opposite numbers*. We say that $+2$ is the opposite of -2 and vice versa (we will write '$\overline{-2}$' to mean the opposite of -2).

In order to define addition, let us consider a trip K to D and then from D to L. The trip from K to D corresponds to the directed number $+4$ and the trip from D to L corresponds to the directed number -3. It is reasonable to postulate that combining the two trips corresponds to adding directed numbers and thus (since the trip from K to L corresponds to $+1$) we have: $(+4) + (-3) = (+1)$. Now that we have defined addition, note that the opposite of a directed number could be defined as the number which we must add to the given number to get zero.

The problem of intuitively defining multiplication of directed numbers is considerably more difficult since evidently the model we have just constructed will not work. We must either find a new model or use other considerations to derive a definition which will work. Certainly, if we introduce the concepts of time and rate into our previous model, we then have some hope of multiplying directed numbers since rate multiplied by time equals distance.

Let us designate time changes by assuming that time flows as it does in the physical world (i.e., from the present to the future) and designate rate changes by assigning to the rate a plus sign or a minus sign depending on whether a moving object is moving to the right or to the left. Thus the symbol '$+2$' will stand for a time change of two hours, for example, and also will stand for a rate of two miles per hour to the right. Thus '$(+3)(+2)$' is a name for a trip of six units to the right (or to refer to the original model '$+6$'). We write this: $(+3)(+2) = (+6)$. Using the same reasoning, $(-3)(+2) = (-6)$. Since time multiplied by rate equals distance is also true, we can also define $(+2)(-3) = (-6)$ and thus have covered all of the possible cases but one.

An attempt to assign an intuitive meaning to $(-3)(-2)$ leads us immediately into difficulty since it involves the physically impossible idea of time running backwards. However, the situation is not too hopeless since we can make use of an idea first expressed by Hermann Hankel in 1867 called "The Principle of Permanence of Formal Laws", which essentially says that we as humans tend to employ rules under more general circumstances than are warranted by the derivation of these rules. To illustrate, consider the following sequence of equalities:

$$(-2)(+4) = (-8)$$
$$(-2)(+3) = (-6)$$
$$(-2)(+2) = (-4)$$
$$(-2)(+1) = (-2)$$
$$(-2)(\ \ 0) = (\ \ 0)$$

Evidently if we want to continue the pattern, we must define $(-2)(-1) = (+2)$. There is no justification for this definition, other than the fact that it is expedient to make it as we have. If more justification is needed, suffice it to say that this definition allows us to make one rule for the multiplication of directed numbers whereas any other definition makes it necessary to consider special cases. It can also be said that this definition is necessary if our model is to satisfy the distributive law.

As we have mentioned previously, any attempt to prove that the intuitive numbers which we have defined actually are a model of the axiom system is due to fail because of the rather vague notions which have been used in the construction of these numbers. We can, however, try as many cases as possible in the hope that we will be convinced that the numbers which we constructed are indeed a model of the axiom system. We need only to remark here that if we do try many cases we will find that our intuitively constructed model does indeed seem to be a model of the axioms listed at the beginning of this section.

PROBLEMS

3.1.1 How many interpretations are there of $a + b + c + d$?
List all these interpretations and prove they are all equal. (Remember that addition is a binary operation, i.e., it is defined only for two numbers.)

3.1.2 Prove (using the axioms)

$$\forall a \; \forall b \; \forall c \; \forall d, \quad (a + b)(c + d) = ac + bc + ad + bd.$$

3.1.3 Prove

$$\forall a, \quad a \cdot 0 = 0.$$

3.1.4 Prove

$$\forall a, \quad (-1) \cdot a = \bar{a}.$$

3.1.5. Prove

$$\forall a, \forall b, \quad \bar{a} \cdot \bar{b} = a \cdot b.$$

3.2 SUBTRACTING DIRECTED NUMBERS

When we first learned subtraction in grade school, it is probable that we learned it by using addition. For example, if we were given a problem:

$$\begin{array}{r} 7 \\ -4 \\ \hline ? \end{array}$$

most of us asked ourselves the question: $4 + ? = 7$. To put it in a slightly different way: '7 − 4' is a name of a number which when added to 4 gives us 7. [Symbolically: $(7 - 4) + 4 = 7$]

Suppose now that we wish to subtract $+7$ from -5. We know that

$$(+7) + [(-5) - (+7)] = -5$$

by the definition of subtraction as the inverse operation of addition. We also know (since $(+7) + (-7) = 0$) that

$$(-5) + [(+7) + (-7)] = -5$$

But by the associative and commutative laws we have:

$$(-5) + [(+7) + (-7)] = [(-5) + (+7)] + (-7)$$
$$= [(+7) + (-5)] + (-7)$$
$$= (+7) + [(-5) + (-7)]$$

and comparing

$$(+7) + [(-5) - (+7)] = -5$$

with

$$(+7) + [(-5) + (-7)] = -5$$

we have

$$(-5) - (+7) = (-5) + (-7) = -12.$$

PROBLEMS

3.2.1 Using the method above, write in the simplest form you can, $(-17) - (-8)$.

3.2.2 Prove (as rigorously as possible):

$\forall x \forall y$, if x and y are directed numbers, then $x + \bar{y} = x - y$.

3.3 ORDERING DIRECTED NUMBERS

When we picked a direction on the road, we essentially picked a subset of the set of all directed numbers, and we designated all numbers which corresponded to trips to the right by prefixing a '$+$' to a name for the counting number which told us how many miles. We were picking a set of directed numbers which we will call the *positive directed numbers*. Since 0 has no direction, we shall not call it a positive number. The set of directed numbers that have the opposite direction we will call the **negative directed numbers**, and again, 0 is not a negative number. Thus the directed numbers are split into three classes: positive, negative, and zero. Notice that each number will belong to one and only one of these sets.

If we were dealing with an axiomatic system, we should have to introduce an axiom which accomplished the division above (the reader should try to word such an axiom).

Positive directed numbers have the property of closure under $+$ and $\cdot$ (i.e., the sum of two positive numbers is positive, as is their product). Also, the opposite of a positive directed number is a negative directed number, and the opposite of a negative directed number is a positive directed number. (In fact, we could have defined negative numbers: $\forall\, x$, $\bar{x}$ *is positive* means x *is negative*.)

When we are doing arithmetic in the Fourth grade and want to compare two numbers, we have a very simple device. We try to subtract one of the numbers from the other and we can tell which of the numbers is larger depending upon whether we can subtract or not. This device does not work if we are working with directed numbers because, as we have seen, it is always possible to subtract directed numbers. The idea, however, is essentially the same with directed numbers as above and we define:

$\forall\, x\, \forall\, y$, if x and y are directed numbers, then x *is greater than y* (written $x > y$ or $y < x$) if $x - y$ is a positive directed number.

We will list several properties of '$>$' below; the proof of these properties, from the definition of '$>$' and from the properties of directed positive numbers, we will leave to the reader.

1) $\forall\, x$, if x is positive then $x > 0$ and conversely.
2) $\forall\, x$, x is negative $\Leftrightarrow x < 0$.

3) $\forall x \forall y \forall z, x > y \land y > z \Rightarrow x > z.$

4) $\forall x \forall y \forall z, x > y \Rightarrow x + z > y + z.$

5) $\forall x \forall y \forall z, x > y \land z > 0 \Rightarrow xz > yz.$

6) $\forall x \forall y$, if x and y are directed numbers, then exactly one of the following conditions holds:

$$x > y \quad \text{or} \quad x < y \quad \text{or} \quad x = y.$$

7) $\forall x \forall y, x > y \Rightarrow \bar{x} < \bar{y}.$

Property 6 above leads us to consider the meaning of the symbol '$\not<$'. Since there are three conditions, the negation of one of them leaves us with the possibility of either of the remaining two. Thus: $\forall x \forall y$, if $x \not< y$ then $x > y \lor x = y$. We introduce a new symbol to stand for the compound sentence $x > y$ or $x = y$: we write '$x \geqslant y$'.

PROBLEMS

True or false:

3.3.1 $-10 > +8.$

3.3.2 $-6/-3 > +2.$

3.3.3 $+7 > -14.$

3.3.4 $+1 > 0.$

3.3.5 $-1.53 < +.0001.$

3.3.6 $+10 > (\overline{-10}).$

3.3.7 $+100 > -100.$

3.3.8 Prove Properties 1, 3, 5 and 7 above.

3.4 THE NUMBER LINE

Since we now know how to use '$>$' and '$<$' with directed numbers, we may think of the directed numbers as arranged along a line in order with, for example, '$<$' having the same meaning as 'to the left of'. The point that is labeled '−1', for example, can be thought of as the end point of a trip of −1 units starting at the point labeled '*O*'. For this reason, the point labeled '*O*' is

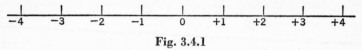

Fig. 3.4.1

often called the *origin*. The point which corresponds to the number +2 is called the *graph* of +2 and the number +2 is called the *coordinate* of that point. Thus the number line can be defined as a line consisting of points each of which corresponds to a directed number. Each point is the graph of the corresponding directed number and each directed number is the coordinate of the corresponding point.

3.5 ABSOLUTE VALUE

Now that we have ordered the directed numbers, we are able to show that −100 < +5, for example. Considered in terms of trips, this is a rather strange idea in view of the fact that if we are going to take a trip in a car, the trip corresponding to −100 will take more gas than the trip corresponding to +5, even though −100 is smaller than +5. In order to talk about the gasoline used we need an idea called the *absolute value* of a directed number. We will define the concept formally a little later but essentially the absolute value is a correspondence between the set of all directed numbers and the set of non-negative directed numbers which can best be exhibited by some examples:

> the absolute value of +6 is +6.
> the absolute value of −6 is +6.
> the absolute value of +1.6 is +1.6.
> the absolute value of −3.75 is +3.75.
> the absolute value of 0 is 0.

We will want to shorten the sentence above, and so we write '$|x|$' to mean *the absolute value of x*.

Now, any directed number determines a pair of numbers, namely, the number and its opposite. We see that the absolute value of a directed number is the positive one of the pair determined by the number. We can state this a little more explicitly as follows:

$$\forall x, \qquad |x| = \text{maximum of } x \text{ and } \bar{x}.$$

Notice that if x is positive, $|x| = x$ (since when x is positive, $\bar{x}$ is negative); if x is negative, $|x| = \bar{x}$ (since if x is negative, $\bar{x}$ is positive); this fact can be used to define absolute value in a slightly different way:

$$|x| = x \quad \text{if} \quad x \geqslant 0$$
$$= \bar{x} \quad \text{if} \quad x < 0.$$

PROBLEMS

Insert '>', '<' or '=' between the following pairs of numerals so that the resulting statement is true:

3.5.1 $|+5| \quad |+3|$.

3.5.2 $|-5| \quad |+3|$.

3.5.3 $|0| \quad |-7|$.

3.5.4 $|-6/10| \quad +2/5$.

3.5.5 $|-8/12| \quad -3/4$.

3.5.6 $-4.3 \quad |-4.3|$.

3.6 MATHEMATICAL CONFUSION

You are all aware that we have been using the symbols '+' and '−' in two different senses. First of all, the symbols have been used to indicate the operations of addition and subtraction. Secondly, when we introduced the idea of a directed number we used the symbols '+' and '−' as prefixes on the names of the counting numbers to indicate a direction. With these two meanings, it is possible for us to have sentences like: $+2 - -3 = +5$. We reduced the possibility of confusion by inserting parentheses, but even if we hadn't, most of us would have been able to tell the meaning of '$+$' or '$-$' from the context. The preceding confusion is bad enough, but mathematicians have compounded the confusion by introducing still another use of the symbol '$-$'. In place of the symbol '$\frown$' we use the symbol '$-$'. That is, for the symbol '$\overline{-3}$' (meaning the opposite of -3), we write '$-(-3)$'. Thus we can have sentences like the following: $+3 - - -3 = 0$. Again, parentheses would help to clear up some of the confusion and we will use them where we think they would help.

With this notation, some of the theorems of the previous sections appear as follows:

$$\forall \, x, \text{ if } x \text{ is positive, } -x \text{ is negative.}$$
$$|x| = x \text{ if } x \text{ is positive.}$$
$$= -x \text{ if } x \text{ is negative.}$$

PROBLEMS

For each of the following expressions write another so that the two expressions name opposite numbers whenever the variables are replaced by names of numbers:

3.6.1 y.

3.6.2 $-(-x)$.

3.6.3 $y - x$.

3.6.4 $x - y$.

3.6.5 $x + y$.

3.6.6 $|x - y|$.

3.6.7   True or false:

    a) $\forall \, x$, $-x$ is negative.
    b) $\forall \, x$, $-x$ is positive $\Rightarrow x$ is negative.
    c) $\forall \, x$, $x = 0 \Rightarrow -x = 0$.
    d) $\forall \, x$, $-x$ is negative $\Rightarrow x$ is positive.

3.7   EQUATIONS AND INEQUALITIES

We define an equation to be an open sentence whose verb is $=$. An inequality is an open sentence whose verb is $<$ or $>$ or $\leqslant$ or $\geqslant$.

Consider the equation $x + 1 = 0$. This equation determines a set (called the solution set of the equation) which consists of all those numbers which satisfy the equation. Notice that the equation $x = -1$ also determines the same solution set as $x + 1 = 0$. Equations which have the same solution set are said to be *equivalent equations.*

In some sense, the name '$\{x|x = -1\}$' is a simpler name for the solution set than the name '$\{x|x + 1 = 0\}$'. We are going to investigate how we can find a simpler (or at least a different) name for the solution set of an equation. Some of the ways are already apparent. For example: if we add the same number to both sides of an equation, the resulting equation is equivalent to the given equation (why?); or if we multiply both sides of an equation by the same non-zero number, the resulting equation is equivalent to the given equation (why?). Thus we see that $\{x|2x - 5 = 7\}$ is the same as $\{x|x = 6\}$. These methods, strong as they are, will not work if we have $\{x||x| = +2\}$. This is so primarily because the definition of $|x|$ is a compound sentence rather than a simple sentence. Let us consider the reasoning involved in finding a simpler name for the solution set of $|x| = +2$. Before we start, we should realize that the definition of $|x|$ requires us to consider cases; namely, we must consider the case where x is non-negative ($x \geqslant 0$) and also the case where x is negative ($x < 0$). There is a tautology which we can apply to argue by cases which states:

$$[(P \wedge Q) \vee (P \wedge \sim Q)] \Leftrightarrow P;$$

thus:

$$\{x||x| = +2\} = \{x|(|x| = +2 \wedge x \geqslant 0) \vee (|x| = +2 \wedge x < 0)\}$$

Applying the definition of $|x|$, we have:

$$\{x||x| = +2\} = \{x|(x = +2 \wedge x \geqslant 0) \vee (-x = +2 \wedge x < 0)\}$$
$$(\text{why?})$$
$$= \{x|x = +2 \wedge x \geqslant 0\}$$
$$\cup \{x| -x = +2 \wedge x < 0\} \qquad (\text{why?})$$

$$= (\{x|x = +2\} \cap \{x|x > 0\})$$
$$\cup (\{x| - x = +2\} \cap \{x|x < 0\}) \qquad \text{(why?)}$$
$$= \{x|x = +2\} \cup \{x|x = -2\} \qquad \text{(why?)}$$
$$= \{+2\} \cup \{-2\} \qquad \text{(why?)}$$
$$= \{+2, -2\}$$

As you might suspect, no mathematician goes through all these steps, but it is advisable for you to do so until you are able to do the problems.

PROBLEMS

Give another name for solution sets of the following sentences:

3.7.1 $|x| = \bar{x}$.

3.7.2 $|x| = +2$.

3.7.3 $|x/x| = x/x$.

3.7.4 $|-2 \cdot x| = 2 \cdot |x|$.

3.7.5 $|x| = -4$.

3.7.6 $|x^2| = |x|^2$.

3.7.7 $|x| < 1$.

3.7.8 $|x| \leqslant 2$.

3.7.9 $|x| > 1$.

3.7.10 $|x - 1| \leqslant 1$.

3.7.11 $|x + 2| > 1$.

3.7.12 $x \leqslant |x|$.

3.8 GRAPHS

We have already talked about the number line and about the fact that to each directed number there corresponds a point on the number line, called the graph of the directed number. Now, since solution sets of equations and inequalities consist of directed

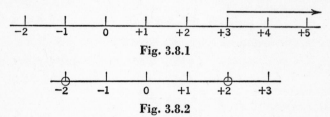

Fig. 3.8.1

Fig. 3.8.2

numbers, we can talk about the graph of a solution set. This graph is called the *locus* of the equation or inequality. For example, the locus of the inequality $x > +3$ consists of all the points which have coordinates greater than three (Figure 3.8.1). In the previous section, we found a simple name for the solution set $\{x||x| = +2\}$. The graph of this set is shown in Figure 3.8.2.

PROBLEMS

Find simpler names for the following sets and graph each set (Note: in the following we will follow the usual practice of writing '3' instead of '+3'.):

3.8.1 $\{x|2x + 1 = 3\}$.

3.8.2 $\{x|x < 2\}$.

3.8.3 $\{x|x < 1 \wedge x > -4\}$.

3.8.4 $\{x|x^2 = 9\}$.

3.8.5 $\{s||s - 3| = 2\}$.

3.8.6 $\{t|t > t + 1\}$.

3.8.7 $\{x|2x + 1 = 3x\}$.

3.8.8 $\{r|r^2 < 9\}$.

3.8.9 $\{q|q^2 \geqslant 9\}$.

3.8.10 $\{x||x| < 5\}$.

3.8.11 $\{x||x| > -6\}$.

3.8.12 $\{t|-2t \leqslant 6\}$.

3.8.13 $\{x|x(x - 1) = 0\}$.

3.8.14 $\{x|x(x - 1) \geqslant 0\}$.

3.8.15 $\{y|y(y - 1) < 0\}$.

3.8.16 $\{x|(3x - 2)(6 - 5x) < 0\}$.

3.8.17 $\{x|(x - 1)(x - 2)(x - 3) = 0\}$.

3.8.18 $\{z|(z - 1)(z - 2)(z - 3) < 0\}$.

3.8.19 $\{x|(x - 3)(x - 2) < 6\}$.

3.8.20 $\{x||x^2 + x - 9| < 3\}$.

4

Ordered Pairs, Functions, and Relations

4.1 ORDERED PAIRS

Suppose that we wish to hide a treasure so that we will be able to find it again. We could draw a map of the area where we hid the treasure, marking its location on the map with a large 'X', or we could designate a reference point (a large rock, for instance) and tell the searcher the location of the treasure by saying: "Two paces north and seven paces east." Note that if we give the distance to the north first it is material which number comes first. If the searcher goes 7 paces north and 2 paces east, he will not find the treasure. We have introduced the concept of an *ordered pair* of numbers. We introduce the notation (2,7) to stand for the ordered pair which has 2 as its first element and 7 as its second element. You are all familiar with this idea, and we will not labor the point here except to note that the beginner will need lots of practice in order to become familiar with the idea that ordered pairs allow us to find our way in a plane once we have determined a starting point. To put it more precisely: to each ordered pair of numbers, there corresponds a point in the plane called the *graph* of the ordered pair, and to each point in the plane, there corresponds an ordered pair of numbers. The numbers in the ordered pair are called the *coordinates* of the point.

Any pair of sets of numbers, A and B, can give us a set of ordered pairs of numbers by considering all pairs which can be formed by taking the first member of the ordered pair from A and the second from B. This set of ordered pairs is called the *Cartesian product* of A and B (written $A \times B$). Thus, for example, if $A = \{1,2\}$ and $B = \{1,2,3\}$, then $A \times B = \{(1,1), (1,2), (1,3), (2,1), (2,2), (2,3)\}$. We can construct the graph of $A \times B$ in the usual way by determining a starting point (called the *origin*) and plotting the points. Such a set of points is called a *plane*

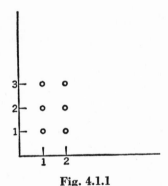

Fig. 4.1.1

lattice. Again note that there is exactly one point of the plane corresponding to each element of $A \times B$, and there is exactly one element of $A \times B$ corresponding to each point of the plane lattice!

Since we are already familiar with the notation for naming sets, we could define $A \times B$ by:

$$A \times B = \{(x,y) | x \in A \land y \in B\}$$

Note that $A \times B$ could also be defined by:

$$A \times B = \{(y,x) | y \in A \wedge x \in B\}$$

PROBLEMS

Given the sets $A = \{1,2,3\}$, $B = \{1\}$, $C = \{2,4,6,8\}$, $D = \{x | x > 0\}$, $E = \{x | |x| < 1\}$, graph the following sets:

4.1.1 $A \times B$.	4.1.6 $C \times E$.
4.1.2 $A \times C$.	4.1.7 $B \times B$.
4.1.3 $C \times A$.	4.1.8 $D \times D$.
4.1.4 $B \times C$.	4.1.9 $E \times D$.
4.1.5 $D \times C$.	4.1.10 $E \times E$.

4.2 OPEN SENTENCES IN TWO VARIABLES

Along with the idea of ordered pairs comes the idea of open sentences containing two variables. Such sentences are not new to us; for example, "He is first and she is second," is such a sentence.

The remarks which we made about open sentences with one variable apply also to those with two variables. In particular, open sentences with two variables serve as "set selectors." The solution set of such open sentences consists of all the ordered pairs which satisfy the open sentence. One remark needs to be made, however. We must know which of the variables holds a place for the first element of an ordered pair. This is usually left to custom, for example in the open sentence $2x + y = 1$ it is understood that the symbol 'x' is the place holder for the first element of the ordered pair. Thus, $(-1,+3)$ belongs to the solution set of the sentence above whereas $(+3,-1)$ does not. This is not to say that the reverse can never happen, however. It just means that if the reverse does happen, we must be warned in advance. One way of warning us is to use the notation introduced previously. Thus:

$$(-1,+3) \in \{(x,y)|2x + y = 1\}$$
$$(+3,-1) \notin \{(x,y)|2x + y = 1\}$$
$$(+3,-1) \in \{(y,x)|2x + y = 1\}$$
$$(-1,+3) \notin \{(y,x)|2x + y = 1\}$$

PROBLEMS

Graph the following sets (by convention, the horizontal axis always corresponds to the first element of an ordered pair):

4.2.1 $\{(x,y)|2x + y = 1\}$.

4.2.2 $\{(x,y)|x + 1 = 0\}$.

4.2.3 $\{x|x + 1 = 0\}$.

4.2.4 $\{(x,y)|y < x - 1\}$.

4.2.5 $\{(x,y)|y > x\}$.

4.2.6 $\{(y,x)|y > x\}$.

4.2.7 $\{(s,t)|s = t\}$.

4.2.8 $\{(r,s)|r = |s|\}$.

4.2.9 $\{(x,y)||x + y| = 1\}$.

4.2.10 $\{(x,y)|x > 1 \wedge y < -2\}$.

4.2.11 $\{(s,t)||s| + |t| = 1\}$.

4.2.12 $\{(x,y)|x^2 + y^2 = 9 \wedge x < 0 \wedge y > 0\}$.

4.2.13 $\{(x,y)|x - 3 = y \wedge y + 2 = -x\}$.

4.2.14 $\{(x,y)|-1 < x < 0\}$ (see note at the top of page 48).

4.2.15 $\{(x,y)|5 < y < 6\}$.

4.2.16 $\{(r,s)|2 < r < 6 \vee -4 < s < -2\}$.

4.2.17 $\{(y,x)|y = x \wedge 2y = 2x - 1\}$.

4.2.18 $\{(x,y)|xy < 1\}$.

4.2.19 $\{(x,y)|x = 0 \vee y = 0\}$.

Note: $-1 < x < 0$ is an abbreviation for the compound sentence $-1 < x \wedge x < 0$. There is *no* abbreviation for the sentence $x > 1 \vee x < 2$.

4.3 LINES AND LINEAR EQUATIONS

If we look at the locus of a linear equation (a *linear equation* is an equation of the form $ax + by + c = 0$, where a, b and c are directed numbers) it seems to us that it forms a line. This is a reasonable conjecture which can be proved even though we will not prove it here.* Any linear equation, $cx + dy + e = 0$, can be transformed into an equivalent equation (if $d \neq 0$) of the form $y = mx + b$ where m is called the *slope* of the line and b is called the *intercept* of the line. (Remember that two equations are equivalent if they have the same solution set.)

Let us consider two linear equations: $ax + by + c = 0$ and $dx + ey + f = 0$. The loci of these two equations either intersect at exactly one point, or have an empty intersection, or are identical. Let us suppose that they intersect at exactly one point, and let us further suppose that we wish to find the coordinates of that point. (In what follows we will abbreviate the open phrase $ax + by + c$ by Rxy, and the open phrase $dx + ey + f$ by Sxy.) As we have mentioned, $Rxy = 0$ has as its locus a line. By the principles which we have mentioned previously, if k is a non-zero directed number, $k \cdot Rxy = 0$ (an abbreviation for $kax + kby + kc = 0$) is an equivalent equation and thus has exactly the same locus as $Rxy = 0$.

Now the equation $kRxy + k'Sxy = 0$ is a linear equation (why?), and thus its locus is a line. Furthermore, the ordered pair of numbers which satisfies both $Rxy = 0$ and $Sxy = 0$ must be the point of intersection of the lines defined by these two

---

* A good proof that the locus of a linear equation is a line is given in K. O. May, *Elementary Analysis* (New York: Wiley, 1950), p. 143.

equations. It follows then that the line defined by $kRxy + k'Sxy = 0$ contains the point of intersection of the lines defined by $Rxy = 0$ and $Sxy = 0$. In our set notation:

$$\forall a \, \forall b, \text{ if } (a,b) \in \{(x,y)|Rxy = 0\}$$
$$\cap \, \{(x,y)|Sxy = 0\}, \text{ then}$$
$$\forall k \, \forall k', \quad (a,b) \in \{(x,y)|kRxy + k'Sxy = 0\}$$

We make use of this fact in solving two linear equations in the following way. Consider the equations: $x + y - 1 = 0$ and $2x - y + 2 = 0$.

Now:

$$\forall a \, \forall b, \text{ if } (a,b) \in \{(x,y)|x + y - 1 = 0\}$$
$$\cap \, \{(x,y)|2x - y + 2 = 0\}, \text{ then}$$
$$\forall k \, \forall k', \quad (a,b) \in \{(x,y)|(k + 2k')x + (k - k')y$$
$$+ (-k + 2k') = 0\}$$

by specialization: (if $k = 1$ and $k' = 1$)

$$\forall a \, \forall b, \text{ if } (a,b) \in \{(x,y)|x + y - 1 = 0\}$$
$$\cap \, \{(x,y)|2x - y + 2 = 0\}, \text{ then}$$
$$(a,b) \in \{(x,y)|3x + 1 = 0\}$$

and further (if $k = 2$ and $k' = -1$):

$$\forall a \, \forall b, \text{ if } (a,b) \in \{(x,y)|x + y - 1 = 0\}$$
$$\cap \, \{(x,y)|2x - y + 2 = 0\}, \text{ then}$$
$$(a,b) \in \{(x,y)|3y - 4 = 0\}$$

From these two sentences we have:

$$\forall a \, \forall b, \text{ if } (a,b) \in \{(x,y)|x + y - 1 = 0\}$$
$$\cap \, \{(x,y)|2x - y + 2 = 0\}, \text{ then}$$
$$(a,b) \in \{(x,y)|x = -\tfrac{1}{3}\} \text{ and}$$
$$(a,b) \in \{(x,y)|y = \tfrac{4}{3}\}.$$

This leads us to the conclusion that

$$\forall a \; \forall b, \text{ if } (a,b) \in \{(x,y)|x + y - 1 = 0\}$$
$$\cap \{(x,y)|2x - y + 2 = 0\}, \text{ then}$$
$$(a,b) = (-\tfrac{1}{3}, \tfrac{4}{3})$$

We have solved the system of linear equations above, and the solution is the ordered pair $(-\tfrac{1}{3}, \tfrac{4}{3})$.

PROBLEMS

Solve as above:

4.3.1 $2x + y = 2$
$3x - 4y = 1.$

4.3.2 $x + y = 2$
$y = 4x - 12.$

4.3.3 Write an equation of the line which contains the intersection of the lines determined by $x - y = 2$ and $2x + y = 1$ and the point $(0,0)$.

4.4 RELATIONS

Up to now, we have regarded an open sentence with two variables as a set selector (i.e., such a sentence determines a set, the set of all ordered pairs which satisfy the sentence) but there is another way of thinking of the same idea. We may think of an open sentence with two variables as expressing a relation which holds between two variables. Since a relation expressed by an open sentence leads to a subset of the set of ordered pairs (formed from a given set A), we will hereafter identify the relation with the subset. Thus: if A is a set, *a relation in A is defined to be a subset of A × A.* We note that since relations are sets of ordered pairs we may graph them.

If R is a relation in A, the subset of A for whose elements x is a placeholder is called the **domain of R.** The subset of A for whose elements y is a placeholder is called the **range of R.** Symbolically: Domain of $R = \{x|(x,y)\in R\}$ and Range of $R = \{y|(x,y)\in R\}$.

PROBLEMS

Let A be the set $\{-1-2,0,1,2,3,4,5\}$. Graph the following relations in A giving the domain and range of each of the relations.

4.4.1 $R_1 = \{(x,y)|x^2 + y^2 \leqslant 5\}$.

4.4.2 $R_2 = \{(x,y)|x^2 = y\}$.

4.4.3 $R_3 = \{(1,1)(1,3)(2,2)(2,3)(2,-1)(5,1)(4,3)(-2,1)(-3,3)\}$.

4.4.4 $R_4 = \{(x,y)|x^2 + y^2 = 4 \wedge y \geqslant 0\}$.

4.4.5 $R_5 = \{(x,y)|x \leqslant y\}$.

4.4.6 $R_7 = \{(x,y)|x = y^2\}$.

4.4.7 $R_8 = \{(x,y)||x + y| = |x| + |y|\}$.

4.5 FUNCTIONS

Look at R_2 and R_4 in Problems 4.4.2 and 4.4.4. Note that these relations enjoy a special property; namely, for each x in the domain there is exactly one y in the range such that the ordered pair (x,y) belongs to the relation. Such relations are called *functions.* Consider the graphs in Figure 4.5.1; each of them determines a relation, but only the first determines a function (why?).

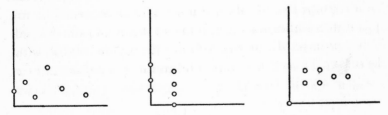

Fig. 4.5.1

To reword the definition: if A is a set, then a function in A is a set of ordered pairs belonging to $A \times A$ such that for each x there is one and only one y for which (x,y) belongs to the function. Graphically this means that a relation R is a function if and only if each vertical line meets the graph of R in not more than one point.

We can generalize this notion slightly by considering two sets, A and B. We define a function from A to B as a subset of $A \times B$ for which we have: each x in A determines at most one y in B such that (x,y) belongs to the function. Similarly we define a relation from A to B as any subset of $A \times B$.

A function F (functions are commonly denoted by F, G, f, g, h, and so forth) associates with each element of its domain a unique element of its range. If we wish to designate this element we will need some special notation. *If $(x,y) \in F$ we write '$y = F(x)$'* (i.e., $F(x)$ is the second element of the ordered pair belonging to F of which x is the first element). For example: if $F = \{(x,y)|y = x^2\}$, then $F(1) = 1, F(2) = 4, F(-1) = 1, F(-7) = 49, F(7) = 49, F(5) = 25$, because $(1,1), (2,4), (-1,1), (-7,49), (7,49)$, and $(5,25)$ are all ordered pairs belonging to the function F.

Although we used a formula to define the function above, it should be noted that this is not at all necessary. A function is completely defined by listing the ordered pairs belonging to it. This may not always be possible, of course, but when it is, there is no necessity for a rule or formula. (We should also note that it is not necessary that a formula be a simple sentence. The function $\{(x,y)|y = |x|\}$ is defined by a compound sentence and we may define even more complicated functions by writing more complicated sentences.) Actually, several of the most used and familiar functions do not have simple formulas which define them explicitly. $y = \sin x$ is one example of such a function.

PROBLEMS

Graph the following functions, giving the domain and range (if the universal set is not specified, it is assumed to be the set of all real numbers):

4.5.1 $\{(x,y)|y = x^2\}$.

4.5.2 $\{(x,y)|y = |x|\}$.

4.5.3 $\{(x,y)|y^2 = x \wedge y \leqslant 0\}$.

4.5.4 Let $F = \{(x,y)|y = x^3 - x^2 + 1\}$.

Find: $F(0)$, $F(2)$, $F(-1)$, $F(\frac{1}{2})$, $F(t)$, $F(1/d)$, $F(2x)$, $F(x + z)$.

4.6 COMPOSITION OF FUNCTIONS

Suppose we have two tables, one a table giving the population of the United States versus the year, and the other a table giving the consumption of corn flakes versus the population. If the tables are complete we should be able to construct a third table giving the consumption of corn flakes versus the year. A table constructed from two other tables is called the **composition** of the two tables. Note that tables must contain a column which is common to the two.

Similarly, given two functions, f and g, we may construct a third function [called the composition of f and g, written '$f(g)$'] if the range of g is a subset of the domain of f. Thus,

if $f = \{(x,y)|y = x^2\}$ and $g = \{(x,y)|y = x + 2\}$,

then

$f(g) = \{(x,y)|y = (x + 2)^2\}$ and $g(f) = \{(x,y)|y = x^2 + 2\}$.

Since we may think of a function as a correspondence between two sets, Figure 4.6.1 may serve to clarify the idea.

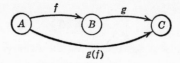

Fig. 4.6.1

PROBLEMS

Given the following pairs of functions, give the range of each, the domain of each, and the two compositions (if possible) of the functions:

4.6.1 $f = \{(1,1), (2,3), (-1,7), (3,3), (0,-2)\}$.
$\quad\; g = \{(1,2), (3,4), (7,7), (-1,6), (-2,6)\}$.

4.6.2 $f = \{(x,y)|y = x\}$.
$\quad\; g = \{(x,y)|x + y = 1\}$.

4.6.3 $f = \{(x,y)|2x + y = 1\}$.
$\quad\; g = \{(x,y)|2y + x = 1\}$.

4.6.4 $f = \{(x,y)|y = x^2\}$.
$\quad\; g = \{(x,y)|y = x^2\}$.

4.6.5 $f = \{(x,y)|x^2 + y^2 = 1 \wedge y \leqslant 0\}$.
$\quad\; g = \{(x,y)|x + y = 1\}$.

4.6.6 $f = \{(x,y)|y = x^3 + x\}$.
$\quad\; g = \{(x,y)|x = y^2 + y\}$.

4.6.7 $f = \{(x,y)|y = 3x + 2\}$.
$\quad\; g = \{(y,x)|y = 3x + 2\}$.

4.7 INVERSE FUNCTIONS

Let us consider the Chicago telephone directory. If we eliminate people who have more than one telephone, this list is a function from the set of people to the set of numbers. It is generally arranged so that the first elements of the ordered pairs in the function are in alphabetical order and this makes finding the function value corresponding to a given person easier. It is possible (even though difficult), however, to read the telephone directory backwards. That is, given a number we can find the person to which this number corresponds. (In fact, the telephone company has a list of numbers written in ascending order so that one can easily read the directory backwards.) This process (backwards table reading) is important enough so that we will consider it further.

Consider the function

$$F = \{(3,5), (-1,5), (0,8), (-2,-10)\},$$

and consider the relation

$$R = \{(5,3), (5,-1), (8,0), (-10,-2)\}.$$

Notice that R was derived from F by interchanging the first and second components of each ordered pair of F (i.e., we have read F backwards). We call R the **inverse** of F (sometimes written F^{-1}). As we can see above, the inverse of a function is not necessarily a function, but in some cases it is. If, for example, we had changed the second ordered pair in F above to $(-1,6)$, then the corresponding relation R would have been a function. Mathematicians sometimes will not refer to the inverse of a function unless the inverse relation also happens to be a function. But this restricts us unnecessarily, and we will refer to the inverse of a function even if the inverse is only a relation. We will have to recognize, however, that almost all of the time our interest will be in finding an inverse *function* if one exists.

The process of finding the inverse relation of a function is quite simple. Let Rxy be an open sentence in two variables such that $\{(x,y)|Rxy\}$ is a function. Since we do nothing more than read a table backwards to find the inverse, we can accomplish this by merely interchanging the roles of 'x' and 'y' in the above sentence. Thus the inverse of $\{(x,y)|Rxy\}$ is $\{(y,x)|Rxy\}$. For example, consider the function $\{(x,y)|y = 2x + 1\}$. The inverse of this function is given by $\{(y,x)|y = 2x + 1\} = \{(x,y)|x = 2y + 1\}$.

PROBLEMS

4.7.1 Find the inverses and graph, and tell whether the following relations and their inverses are functions:

    a) $\{(x,y)|y = x^2\}$.
    b) $\{(x,y)|x + y = 1\}$.
    c) $\{(x,y|y = |x|\}$.
    d) $\{(s,t|s = 4\}$.

4.7.2 Describe a simple way to find the graph of an inverse of a function if you know the graph of the function.

4.7.3 If f is a function such that f^{-1} is also a function, prove that:

$$f(f^{-1}) = f^{-1}(f) = \{(x,y)|y = x\}.$$

4.8 PRINCIPAL VALUES

As we mentioned above, we are interested in finding inverses of functions which are functions. For some functions, our search is doomed before we start, since for example, the inverse of $F = \{(x,y)|y = x^2\}$ is not a function. This is a situation which we would like to remedy if possible, but in order to make a function out of the relation F^{-1} we must do something pretty drastic.

Let us examine the relation R defined by $y^2 = x$ to determine if we can find why it is not a function. Note that $(9,3)$ is one of the ordered pairs in R, as is $(9,-3)$. In fact, $\forall a \forall b$, if $a \geqslant 0$, then $(a,b) \in R \Rightarrow (a,-b) \in R$. If we could somehow throw out all the negative values of the second component of the ordered pairs of R, then for a given value of x there would be only one value of y such that $y^2 = x$. With this accomplished, R would be a function! Symbolically, if $R' = \{(x,y)|y^2 = x \wedge y \geqslant 0\}$ then R' is a function, called the *principal value* of the inverse of F. (Because most people prefer simple sentences to compound sentences, the compound sentence defining R' is usually disguised as a simple sentence: $R' = \{(x,y)|y = \sqrt{x}\}$. This should not, however, be allowed to distract our attention from the fact that R' *must* be defined by a compound sentence in order to be a function.) We should note that $R' \neq R$. In fact, we have destroyed one of the properties which functions and their inverse functions have (see Problem 4.7.3). Even though the composite function $F(R')$ is the identity function—i.e., $F[R'(x)] = x$—it is not the case that $R'(F)$ is the identity function. In more familiar terms, even though $\forall x, (\sqrt{x})^2 = x$, it is not true that $\forall x, \sqrt{x^2} = x$ (why?).

PROBLEMS

4.8.1 $\forall x, \sqrt{x^2} = x$ is false. Can you add something to the open sentence to make it true?

4.8.2 Restrict the variables in the following relations in order to make them functions. If this is not possible, so note:

   a) $\{(x,y)|x + y = 1\}$.
   b) $\{(x,y)|x^2 + y^2 = 1\}$.
   c) $\{(x,y)|x = 1\}$.
   d) $\{(x,y)|y = x^3 + x + 1\}$.

4.8.3 Prove that the inverse of $\{(x,y)|y = ax$ if $a \neq 0\}$ is a function and derive its defining sentence.

4.8.4 A function f is said to be *strictly increasing* if $\forall s \, \forall t$, $s > t \Rightarrow f(s) > f(t)$. (Such functions can be thought of as those whose graph always runs uphill.) Give a proof, or at least a convincing argument, that the inverse of a strictly increasing function is a function.

5

Special Functions

5.1 THE BRACKET FUNCTION

We have not mentioned a very interesting function which is a good example of a function which cannot be defined by a simple formula. The function is defined as $\{(x,y)|y$ an integer $\wedge y \leqslant x < y + 1\}$. The defining sentence can be roughly translated as: "y is the largest integer in x", and is written $y = [x]$. For example: $[\pi] = 3$, $[2] = 2$, $[0] = 0$, $[\sqrt{2}] = 1$, $[-1] = -1$, $[-3.2] = -4$.)

PROBLEMS

Graph the following sets:

5.1.1 $\{(x,y)|y = [x]\}$.

5.1.2 $\{(x,y)|[x + y] = 1\}$.

5.1.3 $\{(x,y)|[x + y] = [x] + [y]\}$.

58

5.1.4 $\{(x,y)|[x + y] = |x + y|\}$.

5.1.5 $\{(x,y)|y = [x]\}$.

5.1.6 $\{(x,y)|y = [x]^2\}$.

5.1.7 $\{(x,y)|y = [x^2]\}$.

5.2 THE EXPONENTIAL FUNCTION

From now on, we will be concerned primarily with the construction of special kinds of functions which are important both to the mathematician and to the user of mathematics. The first such functions are the *exponential functions,* each defined with respect to a non-zero directed number a, called the **base** of the corresponding exponential function. For a given base, the exponential function is defined at first only for the positive integers (i.e., the domain of the function is the set of the positive integers).

If a is a non-zero directed number, we define:

$$f(x) = a \qquad \text{if } x = 1$$
$$= a \cdot f(x - 1) \qquad \text{if } x \neq 1$$

Notice that the definition is a peculiar one when compared to the previous definitions which we have made. It seems at first glance to use f to define f, but a careful study of the definition will soon convince you that the definition does indeed define f for all positive integral values of x. For example: $f(2) = a \cdot f(1) = a \cdot a$. [The reader should, for his own instruction, attempt to evaluate $f(3)$, $f(5)$, and $f(10)$.] By convention, we usually write, as an abbreviation: $f(x) = a^x$ (x is called an **exponent**).

A word here about the definition; note that it has the peculiar property that once we know $f(x)$, we are able to find $f(x + 1)$. We can compare the idea behind this definition with the process of climbing a ladder. The definition tells us how to get from one rung to the next and also tells us how to get onto the first rung. It should be obvious that with such an arrangement we can climb to any rung of the ladder which we desire. Such definitions are called **recursive**.

PROBLEMS

5.2.1 Let f be defined by:

$$f(1) = 1$$
$$f(x) = x \cdot f(x - 1)$$

where x is a positive integer.

Find $f(2)$, $f(3)$, and $f(6)$.

5.2.2 Let f be defined by:

$$f(2) = 0$$
$$f(2x) = x + f(2x - 2)$$

where x is a positive integer.

Find $f(4)$, $f(8)$, and $f(12)$.

5.2.3 Construct a recursive definition for a function and evaluate this function for $x = 2, 3, 5, 8$.

5.3 MATHEMATICAL INDUCTION

Properties which make use of the idea of recursiveness are quite common in mathematics and in everyday life. Suppose that on some superhighway the cars are running bumper to bumper at sixty miles per hour. It is evident that if a car in the line has an accident, so will the car immediately following it. If the first car in the line has an accident, then every car in the line will have an accident. To put it slightly differently; if a Ford in the line has an accident, then the Ford's follower will have an accident and this will be true for every car in the line.

Properties which hold for the follower of an object if they hold for the object itself are called **hereditary**. A little thought will convince you that hereditary properties are very much like our ladder-climbing example in the previous section. If a property is hereditary, then we know that if the property holds for a certain object, it must hold for the follower of that object. This idea can be immediately applied to the positive integers, where the follower of an integer x is defined to be $x + 1$. Thus, if we know that a property is true for the first positive integer, and if, furthermore, we know that the property is hereditary under the definition of follower given above, then the property must hold for all integers. Suppose we wish to prove: $\forall\, a \,\forall\, b,\ (ab)^x = a^x b^x$ for all positive integers x.

Now $$(ab)^1 = ab = a^1 b^1 \qquad \text{(by definition)}$$

and since $$(ab)^{k+1} = (ab)(ab)^k \qquad \text{(by definition)}$$

we have:

$$\text{If}\quad (ab)^k = a^k b^k,\quad \text{then}\quad (ab)^{k+1} = (ab)(ab)^k$$
$$\text{(see above)}$$

$$\text{If}\quad (ab)^k = a^k b^k,\quad \text{then}\quad (ab)^{k+1} = (ab)(a^k b^k)$$
$$\text{(see step above)}$$

thus:

$$\text{If}\quad (ab)^k = a^k b^k,\quad \text{then}\quad (ab)^{k+1} = (a \cdot a^k)(b \cdot b^k)$$
$$\text{(comm. and assoc. laws)}$$

or:

$$\text{If}\quad (ab)^k = a^k b^k,\quad \text{then}\quad (ab)^{k+1} = a^{k+1} \cdot b^{k+1}$$
$$\text{(definition)}$$

Thus we have proved that the property expressed by the formula holds for 1, and further that the property is hereditary. Thus the property holds for all the positive integers. Note that the recursive definition given in the previous section is designed to fit into the theory of mathematical induction.

PROBLEMS

Prove the following:

5.3.1 $a^x \cdot a^y = a^{x+y}$ for all positive integers x and y.

5.3.2 $(a^x)^y = a^{xy}$ for all positive integers x and y.

5.3.3 $a^x/a^y = a^{x-y}$ if x and y are positive integers and $x > y$.

       $= 1$ if x and y are positive integers and $x = y$.

       $= 1/a^{y-x}$ if x and y are positive integers and $x < y$.

5.3.4 Let f be a function defined by:

$$f(1) = 1$$
$$f(x) = 2x - 1 + f(x - 1) \text{ when } x \text{ is a positive integer.}$$

Prove that $f(x) = x^2$ for all positive integers.

5.4 EXTENSION OF THE EXPONENTIAL FUNCTION

In Problems 5.3.1, 5.3.2, and 5.3.3 we proved *laws of expo-nents*. Let us consider for a minute the third of these laws. This law is different from the other two in that it takes three sentences to state it completely. This is an unsatisfactory situation to the mathematician, and he gets around it by defining:

$$a^0 = 1$$

(thus, if $x = y$, $a^{x-y} = 1 = a^0$, and with this definition, the sec-ond of our three sentences becomes unnecessary, its function being included in the first sentence). We also define:

$$a^{-x} = 1/a^x$$

(thus, if $x < y$, $a^x/a^y = 1/a^{y-x} = 1/a^{-(x-y)} = a^{x-y}$, and the third is by now unnecessary since it is also included in the first sen-tence).

These two definitions allow us to assign a meaning to a^x if x is any integer (positive, negative, or zero), and thus we have ex-tended the domain of the function defined by $y = a^x$. (We should note here that just because we have defined a^{-3}, for example, it does not follow that these new "exponents" will obey the laws of exponents. That they will obey the third law is obvious, but we must prove in some way that they also obey the first and second in order to use these laws with negative exponents. We will not prove these facts here even though they can be proved fairly easily by using mathematical induction.)

A further extension of the exponential function can be made if we consider what meaning can be assigned to $a^{1/3}$, for example. If we define $a^{1/3} = \sqrt[3]{a}$, we can then note that the second law is at least partially satisfied since we have:

$$\left(\sqrt[3]{a}\right)^3 = (a^{1/3})^3 = a^{3/3} = a^1 = a$$

We further define:

$$a^{p/q} = \sqrt[q]{a^p}$$

(We will henceforth assume that a is positive in order to get away from the difficulties inherent in taking roots of negative numbers.)

As we mentioned above, we *must* prove the laws of exponents for the new exponents which we have defined. Again, we will not prove these facts even though they can be proved. (The reader should try to prove $a^{p/q} \cdot a^{r/s} = a^{p/q+r/s}$.)

We are now able to attach a definite meaning to a^x when x is any rational number. Thus: $2^{1.234}$ means the 1000th root of 2 to the 1,234th power. But we have still to worry about an expression like 2^{π}. Since π cannot be written as the ratio of two integers (i.e., it is irrational), we are unable immediately to interpret the symbol 2^{π}. Before we attempt a definition of 2^{π}, let us consider one of the properties of some of the functions with which we are familiar. The function defined by $y = x^2$ has the property that when x is close to a given number, the values of the function at x are close to the square of that number. For example: (1.9,3.61), (1.99,3.9601), (1.999,3.986001), (1.9999,3.98959001), (2.001,4.004001), and (2.0001,4.00040001) are all ordered pairs belonging to $\{(x,y)|y = x^2\}$. Note that the closer the first element of the ordered pair is to 2, the closer the second element is to 4. Another way of saying the same thing is to say that we can make the value of the function at x as close to 4 as we like by making x sufficiently close to 2. The property which we have just described is called **continuity,** and the function defined by $y = x^2$ is said to be **continuous** at 2. If a function is not continuous it is said to be **discontinuous.** The function defined by $y = [x]$ is discontinuous at 1, for example, because (1,1), (0.9,0), (0.99,0), (0.999,0) are all elements of the function.

For reasons which we won't discuss here, it is desirable, if possible, to define functions in such a way that they are continuous. For this reason, consider the sequence of numbers: 2^3, $2^{3.1}$, $2^{3.14}$, $2^{3.141}$, $2^{3.1415}$, $2^{3.14159}$, and so forth. By taking more and more places in the decimal expansion of π, it seems reasonable to suppose that 2^π is a number which we can approximate as closely as we wish. Actually, the construction of the number 2^π is a task for which we are not prepared, involving, as it does, the concept of limit, which is definitely not within the scope of this book. Suffice it to say that a rigorous mathematical treatment of the ideas involved in the construction of 2^π is possible, and that 2^π is a perfectly definite member of the real number system. The ideas used in the construction of 2^π can also be used in the construction of 2^x where x is any irrational number, and it is true that the laws of exponents hold when the exponents are irrational numbers.

At this point we have succeeded in defining a continuous function, called the exponential function, whose domain is the set of all real numbers and which is defined by $\{(x,y)|y = a^x \text{ if } a > 0\}$.

PROBLEMS

5.4.1 Graph the function defined by $y = 2^x$.

5.4.2 Graph the function defined by $y = (\frac{1}{2})^x = 2^{-x}$.

5.4.3 Graph the function defined by $y = a^x$ if $a = 1$.

5.4.4 Discuss the differences between the functions defined by $y = a^x$ when $a > 1$ and when $0 < a < 1$.

5.5 THE INVERSE OF THE EXPONENTIAL FUNCTION

We have observed (Prob. 4.8.4) that if a function is strictly increasing it has an inverse. Although we haven't proved it, it seems obvious that the exponential function is a strictly increasing function (if $a > 1$) and therefore has an inverse function (which is also strictly increasing if $a > 1$). This function is $\{(x,y)|x = a^y\}$. Where possible, mathematicians like to write the sentence defining a function in the form $y =$ (an expression in x). For this reason, the inverse of the exponential function (called the logarithmic function) is written $\{(x,y)|y = \log_a x\}$, even though the defining sentence is meaningless unless we know that the function being defined is the inverse of the exponential function.

Corresponding to the laws of exponents (i.e., the properties of the exponential function) there are properties of the logarithmic function, called the laws of logarithms. These can be proved by using the fact that the logarithm is the inverse of the exponential. For example: since $a^{\log_a x} = x$ (a property of inverse functions) we have,

$$A = a^{\log_a A} \quad \text{and} \quad B = a^{\log_a B} \qquad \text{which together imply}$$

$$AB = a^{\log_a A} \cdot a^{\log_a B} = a^{(\log_a A + \log_a B)} \qquad \text{(laws of exponents)}$$

But the sentence above simply means:

$$\log_a AB = \log_a A + \log_a B$$

PROBLEMS

5.5.1 Prove $\log_a A^k = k \cdot \log_a A$ for all real numbers k.

5.5.2 Evaluate:

   a) $2^{\log_2 4}$.

   b) $2^{\log_2 9}$.

5.5.3 If $\log_{10} 2 = .3$, $\log_{10} 3 = .5$ and $\log_{10} 5 = .7$, find:

$$\log_{10} \frac{\sqrt{6} \cdot (15)^{2/3}}{24}$$

5.5.4 Graph the functions defined by $y = \log_2 x$ and $y = \log_{1/2} x$ (see Problem 5.4.2).

Bibliography

Allendoerfer, C. B. and C. O. Oakley, *Principles of Mathematics*. New York: McGraw-Hill, 1955.

Committee on the Undergraduate Program of the Mathematical Association of America, *Elementary Mathematics of Sets with Applications*. Buffalo: Mathematical Association of America, 1958.

Courant, R. and H. E. Robbins, *What Is Mathematics?* New York: Oxford University Press, 1951.

Dantzig, Tobias, *Number, the Language of Science?* New York: Macmillan, 1945.

Dresden, A., *An Invitation to Mathematics*. New York: Henry Holt and Co., 1936.

Eves, H. and C. V. Newsom, *An Introduction to the Foundations and Fundamental Concepts of Mathematics*. New York: Rinehart, 1958.

Kasner, E. and J. Newman, *Mathematics and the Imagination*. New York: Simon and Schuster, 1940.

Kemeny, J. G., J. L. Snell, and G. L. Thompson, *Introduction to Finite Mathematics*. New York: Prentice-Hall, Inc., 1957.

Klein, F., *Elementary Mathematics from an Advanced Standpoint— Arithmetic, Algebra, Analysis*. New York: Dover, 1924.

National Council of Teachers of Mathematics, *Twenty-Third Yearbook, Insights into Modern Mathematics*. Washington, D.C.: The National Council of Teachers of Mathematics, 1957.

Rosser, J. B., *Logic for Mathematicians*. New York: McGraw-Hill Book Co., 1953.

Stabler, E. R., *An Introduction to Mathematical Thought*. Cambridge: Addison-Wesley, 1953.

Tarski, A., *Introduction to Logic and to the Methodology of Deductive Sciences*. New York: Oxford University Press, 1946.

Thurston, H. A., *The Number System*. New York: Interscience Publishers, Inc., 1956.

University of Illinois Committee on School Mathematics, *First Course*. Urbana: University of Illinois High School, 1954 (mimeographed).

Whitehead, A. N., *An Introduction to Mathematics*. New York: Henry Holt and Co., 1911.

Young, J. W. A., *Monographs on Topics of Modern Mathematics*. New York: Dover, 1955.

Index

Index

A

Abacus, 7
Absolute value, 38
Addition of directed numbers, 32
Argument:
  definition, 22
  validity, 22
Axioms, 26
  for directed numbers, 30

C

Cartesian product, 45
Complement of a set, 12
Composition of functions, 53
Conjunction of sentences, 17
Continuity of a function, 63, 64

D

Directed numbers:
  absolute value, 38

Directed numbers (*Cont.*):
  addition, 32
  axioms, 30
  graphs, 38, 42
  model for, 31–34
  multiplication, 32–34
  negative, 36
  opposite, 32, 40
  ordered pairs, 44
  positive, 35
  subtraction, 34
  symbols for, 7, 31
Disjunction of sentences, 17
Domain:
  of a relation, 51
  of a variable, 14

E

Empty set, 13
Equality:
  of numbers, 4
  of sets, 11

Equations:
  definition, 42
  equivalence, 42
Equivalence:
  of equations, 42
  of sets, 5
Exponential functions, 59
Exponents:
  definition, 59
  irrational, 63, 64
  laws of, 62
  negative, 62
  rational, 63

F

Function:
  bracket, 58
  definition, 51
  domain, 51
  inverse, 54
  range, 51
Functions:
  composition, 53
  exponential, 59
  logarithmic, 65
  principal values, 56

G

Graphs:
  of directed numbers, 38, 42
  of equations, 43
  of inequalities, 43
  of ordered pairs, 45

H

Hereditary property, 60

I

Implication, 19–21
Inequalities, 35
  graphs, 43

Intersection of sets, 12
Inverse of a function, 54

L

Laws of logic, 23
Linear equations, 48
Lines, 48
Logarithms:
  definition, 65
  laws, 65
Logical connectives, 16
Logical equivalence, 21

M

Mathematical induction, 60
Modern mathematics, 1
Multiplication, 32

N

Negation of a sentence, 17
Number line, 38
Number (*see also* Directed Numbers),
  5

O

One-to-one correspondence, 5
Open sentences, 14
Opposite numbers, 32
Ordered pairs of numbers, 44
  graphs, 45
Ordering of numbers, 35

P

Parentheses, use of, 21
Proof, 28
Properties:
  relation to sentences, 14
  relation to sets, 11

Q

Quantifiers, 25, 26

R

Range of a relation, 51
Recursive definition, 60
Relations:
　definition, 50
　domain, 51
　range, 51

S

Semantics in mathematics, 3
Semi-quotes, use of, 3, 4
Sets:
　complement, 12
　definition, 10
　elements, 10
　equivalence, 5
　intersection, 12
　union, 12

Solution set, 14
Subset, 12
Subtraction, 34

T

Tautology, 22
Theorem, *definition* of, 27
Truth tables, 16–18
Truth value, 16

U

Union of sets, 12
Universal set, 13

V

Validity, 23
Variable, 14